Content Page

Designed to reinforce essential math SKILLS!

By completing this math workbook, your child will gain systematic practice in the following math concepts:

- Ordering numbers
- Counting
- Odd and even numbers
- Place value
- Addition
- Subtraction
- Multiplication
- Division
- Fractions
- Reading and making graphs
- Following directions
- Plotting on a grid
- Shapes
- Non-standard measuring
- Perimeter
- Patterning
- Telling time

Content Development by Demetra Georgopoulos
Illustration and Design by Mike Polito

We acknowledge the financial support of the Government of Canada .

Government of Canada

Canada

PAPP International Inc.© 2006

Math Grade 2

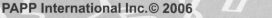

Ordering Numbers

a. Fill in the missing numbers.

1. Just before and after

_25_ , 26 , _27_

2. Just before and after

_70_ , 71 , _72_

3. Just after

50 , 51 , _52_

4. Just before

_26_ , 27 , 28

5. Just after

13 , 14 , _15_

6. Just before

_26_ , 27 , 28

7. Between

34 , _35_ , 36

8. Between

5 , _6_ , 7

9. Between

16 , _17_ , 18

10. Just before and after

_79_ , 80 , _81_

11. Between

45 , _46_ , 47

12. Just after

47 , 48 , _49_

13. Just before

_46_ , 47 , 48

14. Just before and after

_80_ , 81 , _82_

15. Just before

_10_ , 11 , 12

16. Just after

62 , 63 , _64_

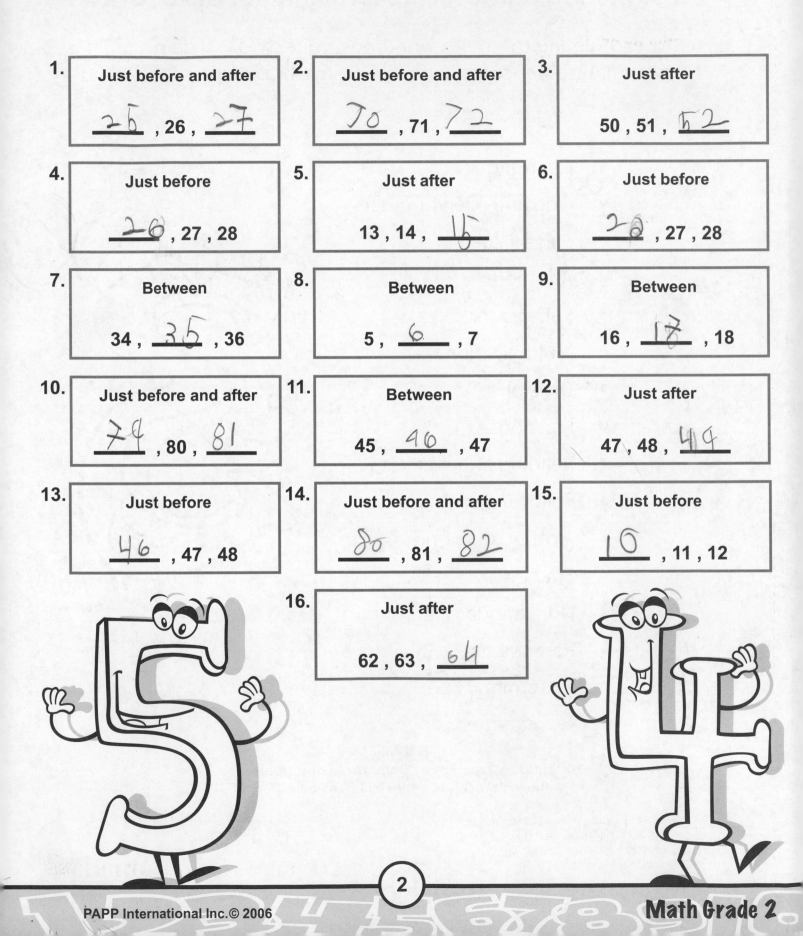

2

Math Grade 2

Skip Counting

a. Fill in the missing numbers to complete the pattern.

1. Skip-count by ones.

54 , 55 , 56 , _57_ , _58_ , _59_

2. Skip-count by twos.

54 , 56 , 58 , _60_ , _62_ , _64_

3. Skip-count by fives.

70 , 75 , 80 , _85_ , _90_ , _95_

4. Skip-count by threes.

12 , 15 , 18 , _21_ , _24_ , _27_

5. Skip-count by twos.

32 , 34 , 36 , _38_ , _40_ , _42_

6. Skip-count by fives.

60 , 65 , 70 , _75_ , _80_ , _85_

7. Skip-count by fours.

10 , 14 , 18 , _22_ , _26_ , _30_

8. Skip-count by threes.

33 , 36 , 39 , _42_ , _45_ , _48_

PAPP International Inc.© 2006

Math Grade 2

Counting

a. Fill in the missing numbers to complete the pattern. **Use the number line to help.**

0 1 2 3 4 5 6 7 8 9 10 11 12 13 14 15 16 17 18 19 20 21 22 23

1. Count backward to 11.

17 , 16 , 15 , 14 , 13 , 12 , 11

2. Count forward to 14.

8 , ____ , ____ , ____ , ____ , ____ , ____

3. Count backward to 17.

23 , ____ , ____ , ____ , ____ , ____ , ____

4. Count forward to 17.

11 , ____ , ____ , ____ , ____ , ____ , ____

5. Count forward to 16.

10 , ____ , ____ , ____ , ____ , ____ , ____

6. Count backward to 14.

20 , ____ , ____ , ____ , ____ , ____ , ____

7. Count backward to 12.

18 , ____ , ____ , ____ , ____ , ____ , ____

8. Count backward to 15.

21 , ____ , ____ , ____ , ____ , ____ , ____

9. Count backward to 7.

13 , ____ , ____ , ____ , ____ , ____ , ____

PAPP International Inc.© 2006

Math Grade 2

a. Connect the dots, counting by tens from 10 to 200.

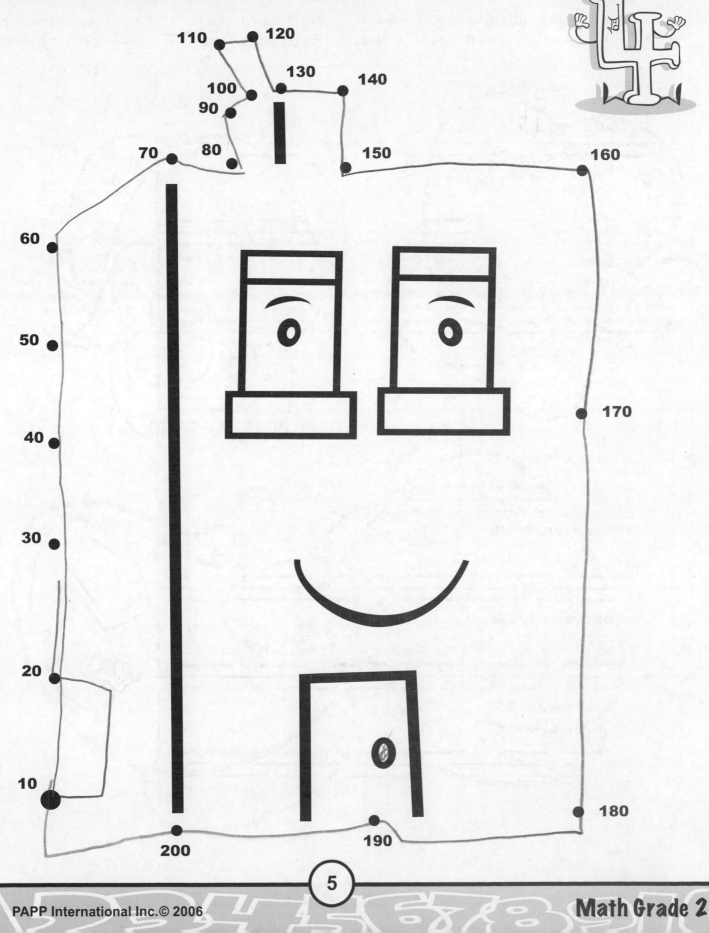

Math Grade 2

Odd and Even Numbers

a. Look at the picture.

Color the spaces with **odd** numbers **red.**
Color the spaces with **even** numbers **blue.**

Odd numbers have 1, 3, 5, 7 or 9 in the ones place.
Even numbers have 0, 2, 4, 6 or 8 in the ones place.

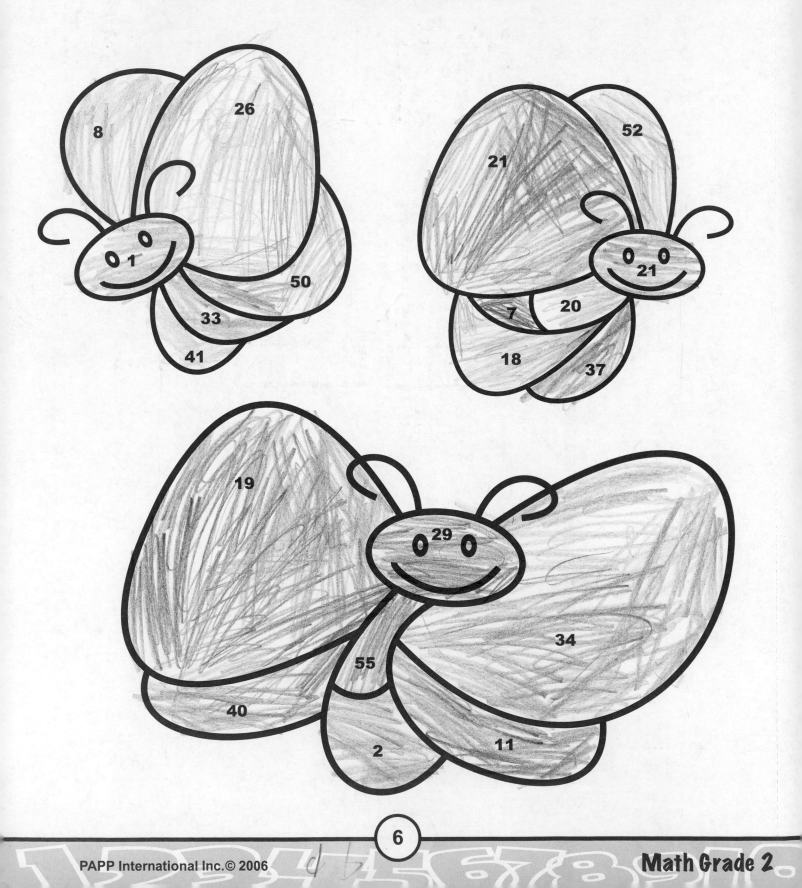

PAPP International Inc.© 2006

Math Grade 2

Tens and Ones

a. Count and then write the tens and ones.

1.

tens [1]   ones [3]

Write the number: [12]

2.

tens [2]   ones [9]

Write the number: [24]

3.

tens [4]   ones [4]

Write the number: [44]

4.

tens [8]   ones [0]

Write the number: [80]

5.

tens [7]   ones [3]

Write the number: [73]

6.

tens [5]   ones [7]

Write the number: [57]

57

b. Count and then write the tens and ones.

1.

70 ones = [7] tens and [0] ones

Write the number: [70]

2.

7 ones = [0] tens and [7] ones

Write the number: [7]

3.

19 ones = [1] tens and [9] ones

Write the number: [19]

4.

18 ones = [1] tens and [8] ones

Write the number: [18]

Math Grade 2

Regroup Ones as Tens

a. Count and then write the tens and ones.

1.

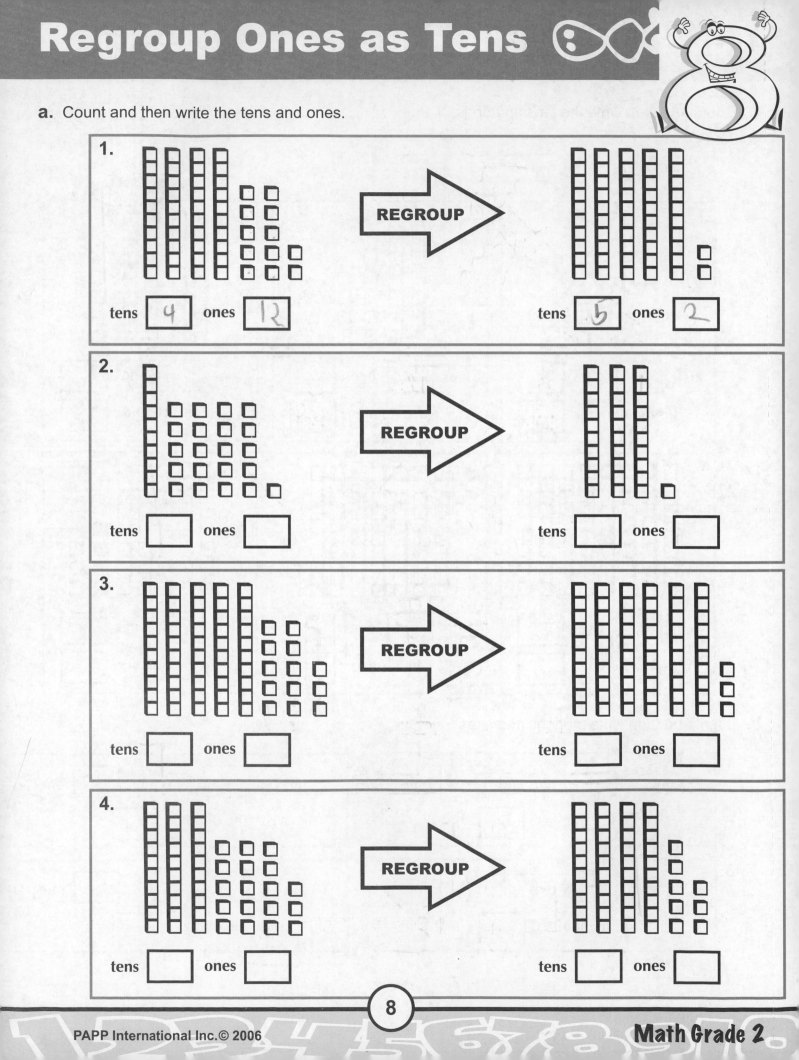

REGROUP

tens `4`   ones `12`   →   tens `5`   ones `2`

2.

REGROUP

tens ☐   ones ☐   →   tens ☐   ones ☐

3.

REGROUP

tens ☐   ones ☐   →   tens ☐   ones ☐

4.

REGROUP

tens ☐   ones ☐   →   tens ☐   ones ☐

PAPP International Inc.© 2006

Math Grade 2

Hundreds, Tens, and Ones

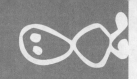

a. Count and then write the tens and hundreds.

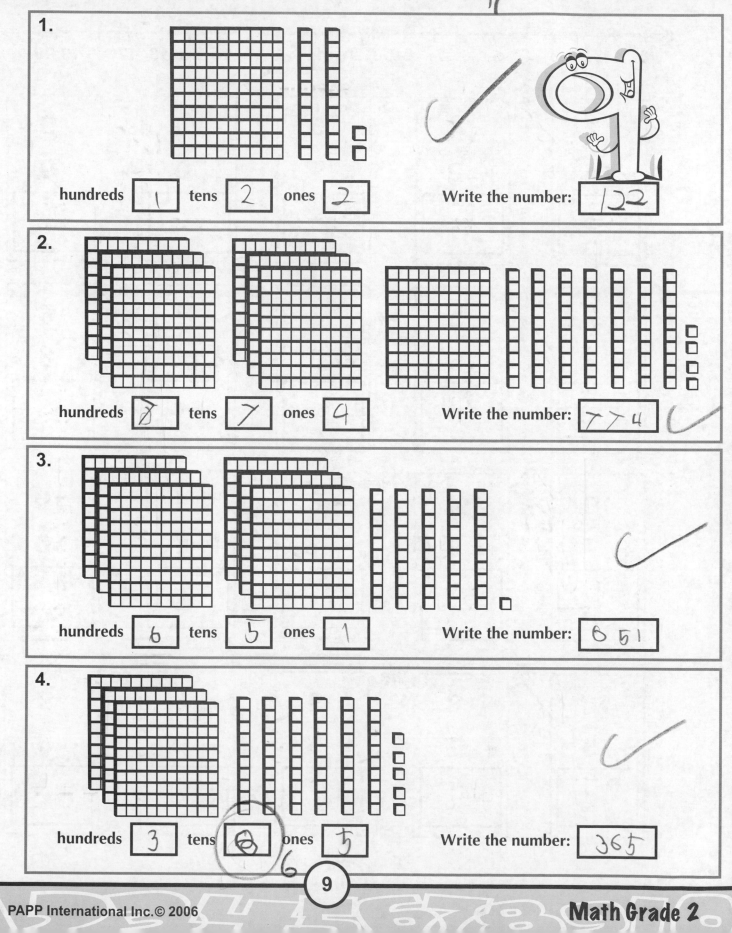

1.

hundreds [1] tens [2] ones [2] Write the number: [122]

2.

hundreds [8] tens [7] ones [4] Write the number: [774]

3.

hundreds [6] tens [5] ones [1] Write the number: [651]

4.

hundreds [3] tens [6] ones [5] Write the number: [365]

Math Grade 2

Addition Fun

a. Complete the following sums. **Use the number line to help.**

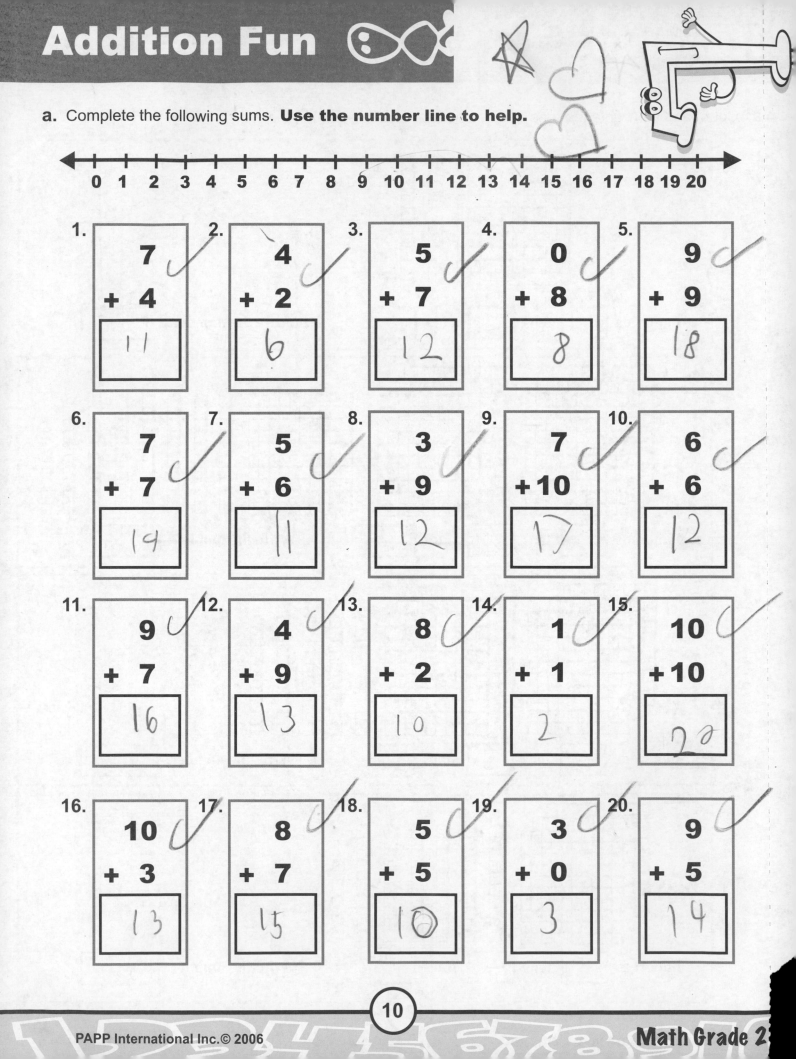

Number line: 0 1 2 3 4 5 6 7 8 9 10 11 12 13 14 15 16 17 18 19 20

1.
$$7 + 4 = 11$$

2.
$$4 + 2 = 6$$

3.
$$5 + 7 = 12$$

4.
$$0 + 8 = 8$$

5.
$$9 + 9 = 18$$

6.
$$7 + 7 = 14$$

7.
$$5 + 6 = 11$$

8.
$$3 + 9 = 12$$

9.
$$7 + 10 = 17$$

10.
$$6 + 6 = 12$$

11.
$$9 + 7 = 16$$

12.
$$4 + 9 = 13$$

13.
$$8 + 2 = 10$$

14.
$$1 + 1 = 2$$

15.
$$10 + 10 = 20$$

16.
$$10 + 3 = 13$$

17.
$$8 + 7 = 15$$

18.
$$5 + 5 = 10$$

19.
$$3 + 0 = 3$$

20.
$$9 + 5 = 14$$

Math Grade 2

Addition Fun

Math Grade 2

a. Fill in the missing number to complete the sums.

1.
$$5 + \boxed{5} = 10$$

2.
$$5 + \boxed{2} = 7$$

3.
$$6 + \boxed{2} = 8$$

4.
$$9 + \boxed{5} = 14$$

5.
$$\boxed{9} + 3 = 12$$

6.
$$5 + \boxed{8} = 13$$

7.
$$\boxed{2} + 2 = 4$$

8.
$$6 + \boxed{6} = 12$$

9.
$$3 + \boxed{7} = 10$$

10.
$$\boxed{5} + 10 = 15$$

11.
$$7 + \boxed{9} = 16$$

12.
$$\boxed{0} + 9 = 9$$

13.
$$3 + \boxed{2} = 5$$

14.
$$5 + \boxed{4} = 9$$

15.
$$\boxed{3} + 5 = 8$$

16.
$$\boxed{7} + 6 = 13$$

17.
$$10 + \boxed{1} = 11$$

18.
$$\boxed{3} + 5 = 8$$

PAPP International Inc.© 2006

Subtraction Fun

a. Complete the following differences. **Use the number line to help.**

Number line: 0 1 2 3 4 5 6 7 8 9 10 11 12 13 14 15 16 17 18 19 20

1.
10
- 6
= 4

2.
15
- 8
= 7

3.
18
- 9
= 9

4.
14
- 8
= 6

5.
11
- 3
= 8

6.
12
- 7
= 5

7.
8
- 1
= 7

8.
6
- 2
= 4

9.
17
- 9
= 8

10.
9
- 4
= 5

11.
14
- 5
= 9

12.
11
- 4
= 7

13.
20
- 11
= 19

14.
7
- 6
= 1

15.
13
- 9
= 4

16.
14
- 7
= 7

17.
16
- 8
= 8

18.
5
- 4
= 1

PAPP International Inc.© 2006

Math Grade 2

Subtraction Fun

a. Fill in the missing number to complete the subtraction fact.

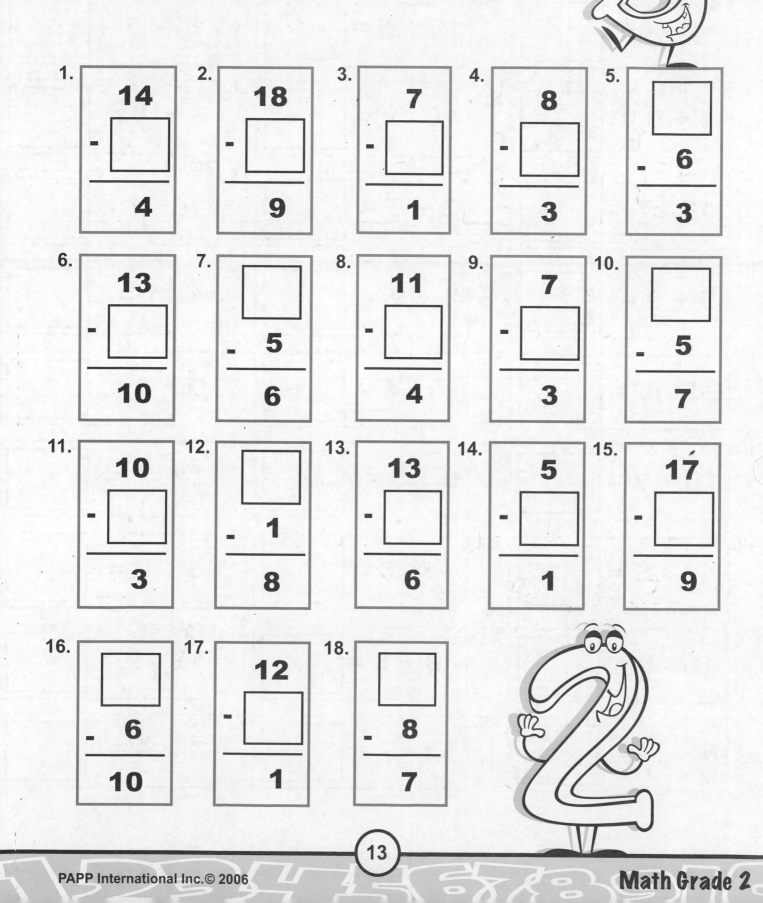

1.
$$14 - \boxed{} = 4$$

2.
$$18 - \boxed{} = 9$$

3.
$$7 - \boxed{} = 1$$

4.
$$8 - \boxed{} = 3$$

5.
$$\boxed{} - 6 = 3$$

6.
$$13 - \boxed{} = 10$$

7.
$$\boxed{} - 5 = 6$$

8.
$$11 - \boxed{} = 4$$

9.
$$7 - \boxed{} = 3$$

10.
$$\boxed{} - 5 = 7$$

11.
$$10 - \boxed{} = 3$$

12.
$$\boxed{} - 1 = 8$$

13.
$$13 - \boxed{} = 6$$

14.
$$5 - \boxed{} = 1$$

15.
$$17 - \boxed{} = 9$$

16.
$$\boxed{} - 6 = 10$$

17.
$$12 - \boxed{} = 1$$

18.
$$\boxed{} - 8 = 7$$

Math Grade 2

More Addition and Subtraction

a. Fill in the missing number to complete the following:

1. 12 - 6 =

2. 10 + 5 = 15

3. 11 - 6 =

4. 4 + 9 =

5. 18 - 9 = 27

6. 3 + 1 =

7. 12 - 7 =

8. 3 + 3 = 2

9. 14 - 8 =

10. 5 + 9 =

11. 1 + 9 =

12. 4 - 1 =

13. 20 - 10 =

14. 5 - 4 =

15. 9 + 3 =

16. 10 + 7 =

17. 0 + 5 =

18. 12 - 7 =

19. 14 - 6 =

20. 13 - 6 =

21. 3 + 9 =

22. 16 - 8 =

23. 9 + 5 =

24. 18 - 9 =

25. 6 + 9 =

26. 13 - 7 =

27. 3 + 4 =

Math Grade 2

What's the Sign?

a. Write a plus (+), or minus (-) sign in the circle to make the number sentence true.

1. $12 \bigcirc 6 = 18$

2. $0 \bigcirc 8 = 0$

3. $7 \bigcirc 4 = 3$

4. $10 \bigcirc 5 = 5$

5. $2 \bigcirc 10 = 12$

6. $14 \bigcirc 8 = 6$

7. $10 \bigcirc 10 = 20$

8. $4 \bigcirc 2 = 2$

9. $7 \bigcirc 2 = 9$

10. $5 \bigcirc 8 = 13$

11. $4 \bigcirc 2 = 6$

12. $9 \bigcirc 4 = 5$

13. $5 \bigcirc 3 = 2$

14. $6 \bigcirc 0 = 6$

15. $7 \bigcirc 2 = 5$

16. $9 \bigcirc 7 = 16$

PAPP International Inc.© 2006

Math Grade 2

Two Digit Addition

a. Find the following sums.

	tens	ones			tens	ones
Step 1				Step 2		
Add the ones column first	**2**	**3**		Add the tens column	**2**	**3**
+	4	5		+	4	5
		8			6	8

1.
```
  14
+ 34
────
  48
```

2.
```
  43
+ 12
────
  55
```

3.
```
  75
+ 24
────
  99
```

4.
```
  50
+ 27
────
  77
```

5.
```
  42
+ 10
────
  52
```

6.
```
  12
+ 55
────
  67
```

7.
```
  23
+ 16
────
  39
```

8.
```
  42
+ 53
────
  95
```

9.
```
  71
+ 18
────
  89
```

10.
```
  24
+ 60
────
  84
```

11.
```
  57
+ 31
────
  88
```

12.
```
  86
+ 12
────
  98
```

13.
```
  50
+ 41
────
  91
```

14.
```
  44
+ 11
────
  55
```

15.
```
  26
+ 30
────
  56
```

16.
```
  34
+ 10
────
  44
```

17.
```
  12
+ 36
────
  48
```

18.
```
  48
+ 11
────
  59
```

19.
```
  63
+ 32
────
  95
```

20.
```
  80
+ 19
────
  99
```

Math Grade 2

a. Find the following sums.

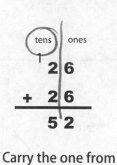

Adding two digit numbers:

- Line up the ones and the tens column.

- Add the ones column, then add the tens column.

- If the sum of the ones column is greater than 9, regroup the ones and carry over to the tens column.

```
 tens | ones
   1
     2 | 6
  +  2 | 6
  ---------
     5   2
```

Carry the one from 12 to the tens column.

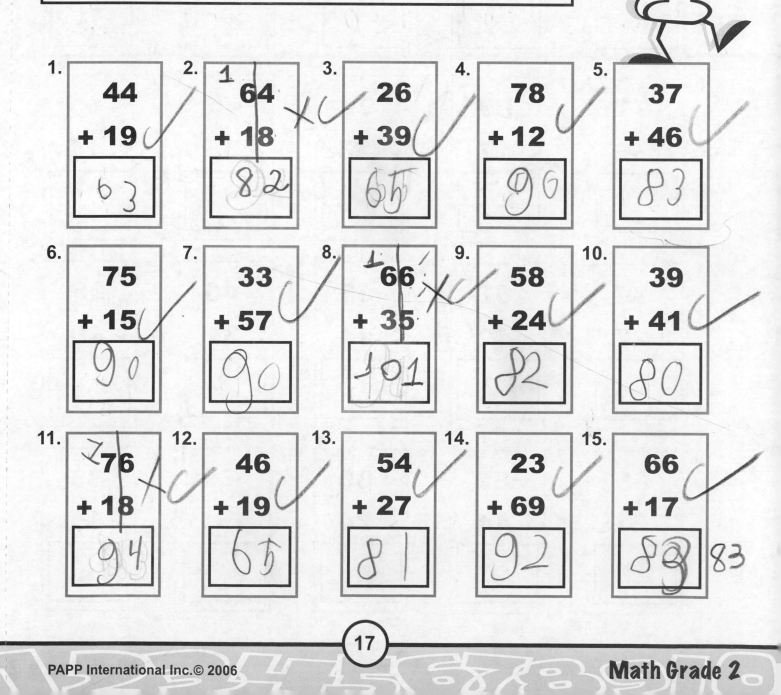

1.
```
  44
+ 19
----
  63
```

2.
```
  64
+ 18
----
  82
```

3.
```
  26
+ 39
----
  65
```

4.
```
  78
+ 12
----
  90
```

5.
```
  37
+ 46
----
  83
```

6.
```
  75
+ 15
----
  90
```

7.
```
  33
+ 57
----
  90
```

8.
```
  66
+ 35
----
 101
```

9.
```
  58
+ 24
----
  82
```

10.
```
  39
+ 41
----
  80
```

11.
```
  76
+ 18
----
  94
```

12.
```
  46
+ 19
----
  65
```

13.
```
  54
+ 27
----
  81
```

14.
```
  23
+ 69
----
  92
```

15.
```
  66
+ 17
----
  83
```

Math Grade 2

Two Digit Subtraction without Borrowing

a. Find the following differences.

> Line up the ones and tens columns when subtracting.
>
> **Step 1**
> Subtract the ones column first
>
> | | tens | ones |
> |---|---|---|
> | | 8 | 7 |
> | - | 4 | 4 |
> | | | 3 |
>
> **Step 2**
> Then subtract the tens column
>
> | | tens | ones |
> |---|---|---|
> | | 8 | 7 |
> | - | 4 | 4 |
> | | 4 | 3 |

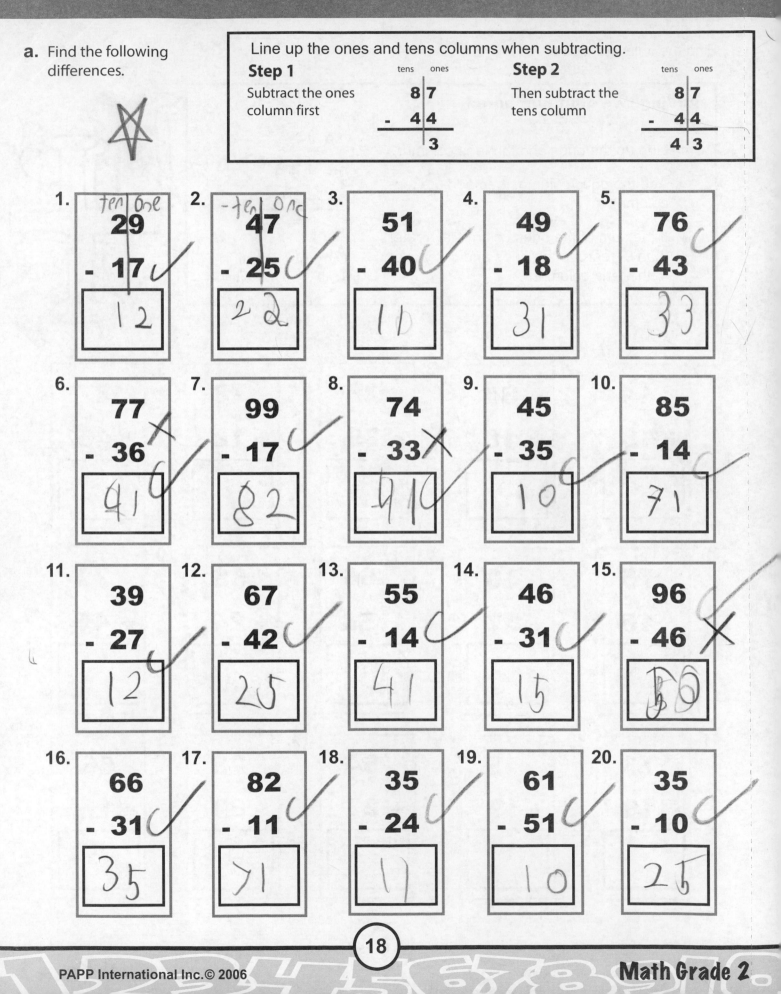

1. ten one
   29
   - 17
   12

2. -ten onc
   47
   - 25
   22

3. 51
   - 40
   10

4. 49
   - 18
   31

5. 76
   - 43
   33

6. 77
   - 36
   41

7. 99
   - 17
   82

8. 74
   - 33
   41

9. 45
   - 35
   10

10. 85
    - 14
    71

11. 39
    - 27
    12

12. 67
    - 42
    25

13. 55
    - 14
    41

14. 46
    - 31
    15

15. 96
    - 46
    50

16. 66
    - 31
    35

17. 82
    - 11
    71

18. 35
    - 24
    11

19. 61
    - 51
    10

20. 35
    - 10
    25

18

Math Grade 2

a. Find the differences.

Subtracting two digit numbers:

- Always line up the ones and the tens.

- Subtract the ones column first, then subtract the tens column.

- When the bottom number of ones column in the equation is greater than the top number, borrow a group of 10 from the tens column.

```
       tens   ones
        3     1
        4     2
      -  3    9
      ─────────
              3
```

You can't take 9 away from 2, so borrow a group of 10 from the 4.

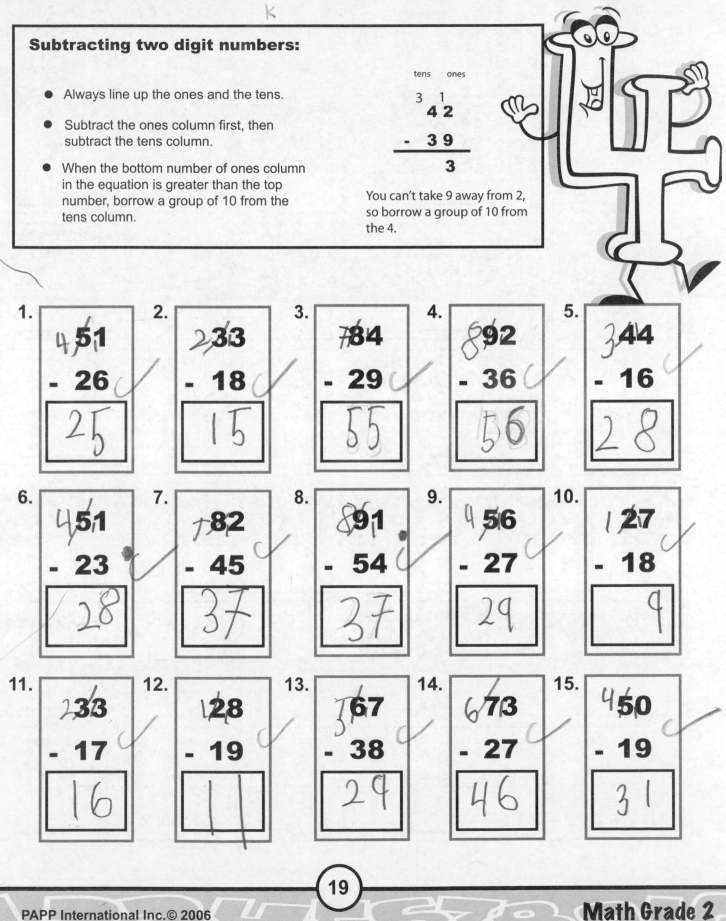

1.
```
  4 5̶1
 -  26
 ─────
    25
```

2.
```
  2̶ 3̶3
 -  18
 ─────
    15
```

3.
```
  7̶ 8̶4
 -  29
 ─────
    55
```

4.
```
  8̶ 92
 -  36
 ─────
    56
```

5.
```
  3̶ 4̶4
 -  16
 ─────
    28
```

6.
```
  4̶ 5̶1
 -  23
 ─────
    28
```

7.
```
  7̶ 82
 -  45
 ─────
    37
```

8.
```
  8̶ 9̶1
 -  54
 ─────
    37
```

9.
```
  4̶ 56
 -  27
 ─────
    29
```

10.
```
  1̶ 27
 -  18
 ─────
     9
```

11.
```
  2̶ 3̶3
 -  17
 ─────
    16
```

12.
```
  1̶ 28
 -  19
 ─────
    11
```

13.
```
  3̶ 67
 -  38
 ─────
    29
```

14.
```
  6̶ 73
 -  27
 ─────
    46
```

15.
```
  4̶ 50
 -  19
 ─────
    31
```

Math Grade 2

Addition and Multiplication

a. Write the sum and then write the product.

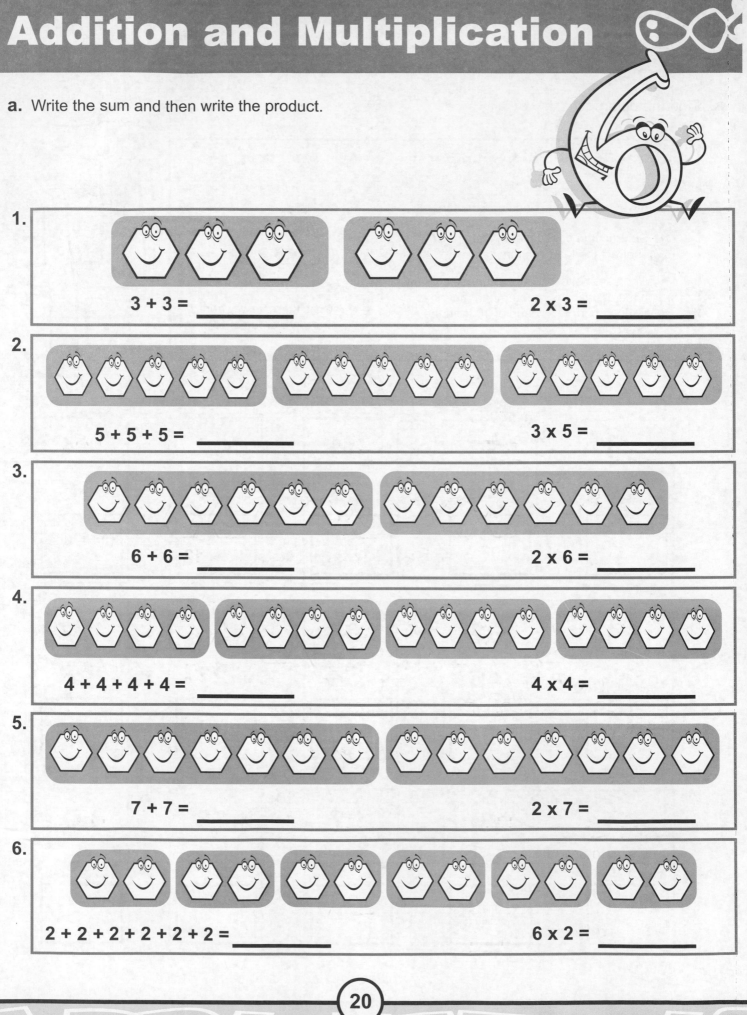

1.

3 + 3 = _____

2 x 3 = _____

2.

5 + 5 + 5 = _____

3 x 5 = _____

3.

6 + 6 = _____

2 x 6 = _____

4.

4 + 4 + 4 + 4 = _____

4 x 4 = _____

5.

7 + 7 = _____

2 x 7 = _____

6.

2 + 2 + 2 + 2 + 2 + 2 = _____

6 x 2 = _____

Math Grade 2

Introducing Division

a. Divide the groups and find the quotient.

1. Divide 12, into groups of 4.

groups: _____4_____   12 ÷ 4 = _____

2. Divide 12, into groups of 2.

groups: _____   12 ÷ 2 = _____

3. Divide 12, into groups of 3.

groups: _____   12 ÷ 3 = _____

4. Divide 10, into groups of 5.

groups: _____   10 ÷ 5 = _____

5. Divide 6, into groups of 2.

groups: _____   6 ÷ 2 = _____

6. Divide 4, into groups of 2.

groups: _____   4 ÷ 2 = _____

Math Grade 2

Fractions

a. What fraction does the colored part show? Circle the fraction.

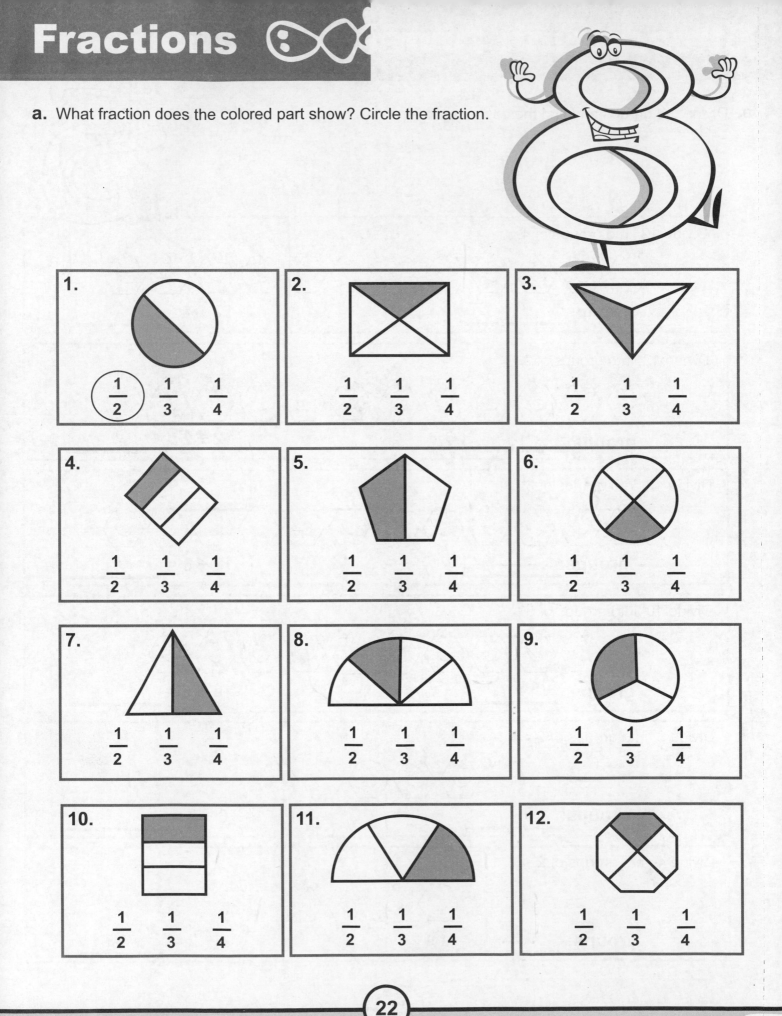

PAPP International Inc.© 2006

Math Grade 2

Show the Fractions

a. Color to show the correct fraction!

1.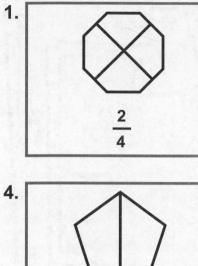
$$\frac{2}{4}$$

2.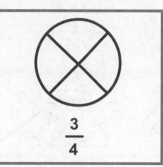
$$\frac{1}{3}$$

3.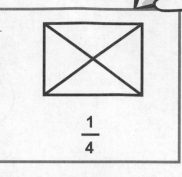
$$\frac{1}{4}$$

4.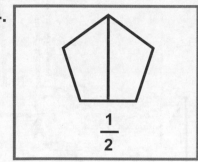
$$\frac{1}{2}$$

5.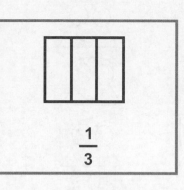
$$\frac{3}{4}$$

6.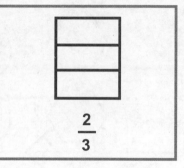
$$\frac{2}{3}$$

b. More fractions.

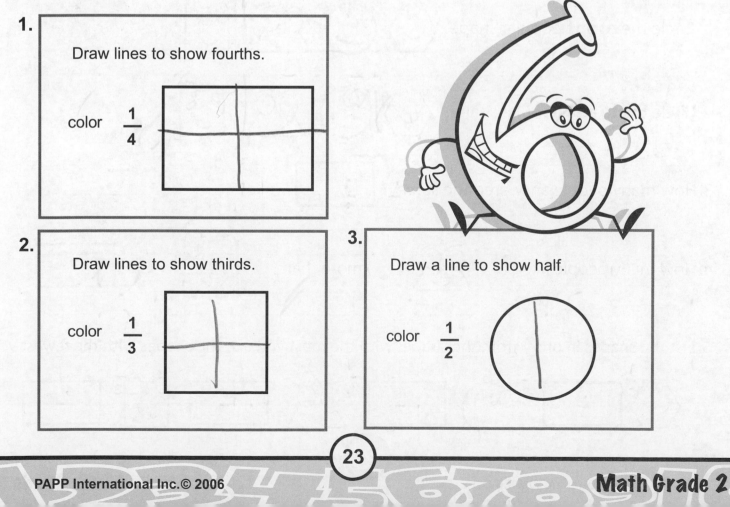

1. Draw lines to show fourths.

color $\frac{1}{4}$

2. Draw lines to show thirds.

color $\frac{1}{3}$

3. Draw a line to show half.

color $\frac{1}{2}$

PAPP International Inc.© 2006

Math Grade 2

Graph 1

a. Use the picture graph to answer the questions.

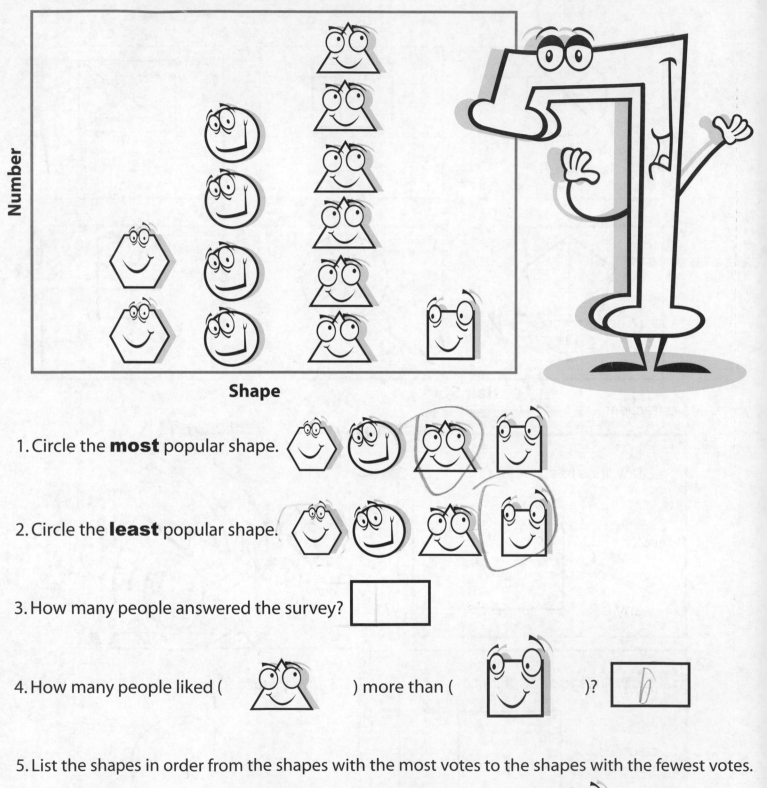

1. Circle the **most** popular shape.

2. Circle the **least** popular shape.

3. How many people answered the survey?

4. How many people liked ( ) more than ( )? 6

5. List the shapes in order from the shapes with the most votes to the shapes with the fewest votes.

2   4   6   1

Math Grade 2

Graph 2

a. Use the picture graph to answer the questions.

Number

Hair Style

1. Circle the **most** popular hair style.

2. Circle the **least** popular hair style.

3. How many people answered the survey?

4. How many people liked ( ) more than ( )? | 3 |

5. List the hair style in order from the hair style with the most votes to the hair style with the fewest votes.

| 3 | 2 | 5 | 5 |

PAPP International Inc.© 2006

Math Grade 2

Graph 3

a. Use the data from the table graph to make a bar graph. Answer the questions.

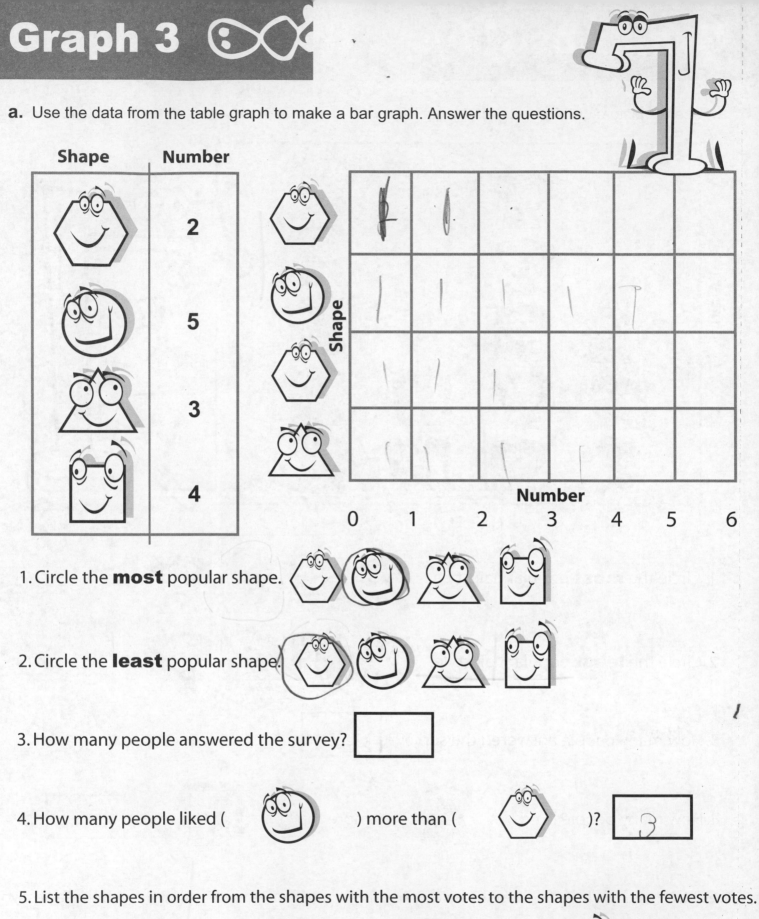

Shape	Number
hexagon	2
circle	5
triangle	3
square	4

1. Circle the **most** popular shape.

2. Circle the **least** popular shape.

3. How many people answered the survey?

4. How many people liked (circle) more than (hexagon)? [3]

5. List the shapes in order from the shapes with the most votes to the shapes with the fewest votes.

| hexagon | 2 | circle | 5 | triangle | 4 | square | 3 |

PAPP International Inc.© 2006   **Math Grade 2**

a. Follow the directions.

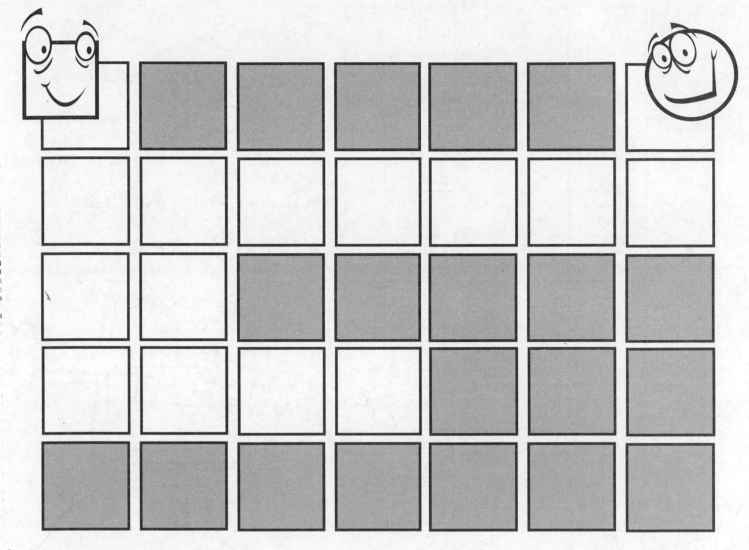

1. Start at the square.

2. Move **down** 3 spaces.

3. Move **right** 3 spaces.

4. Move **left** 2 spaces.

5. Move **up** 2 spaces.

6. Move **right** 5 spaces.

7. Move **up** 1 space.

Math Grade 2

Exploring Grids

a. Draw circles on the grid. The first one has been done for you.

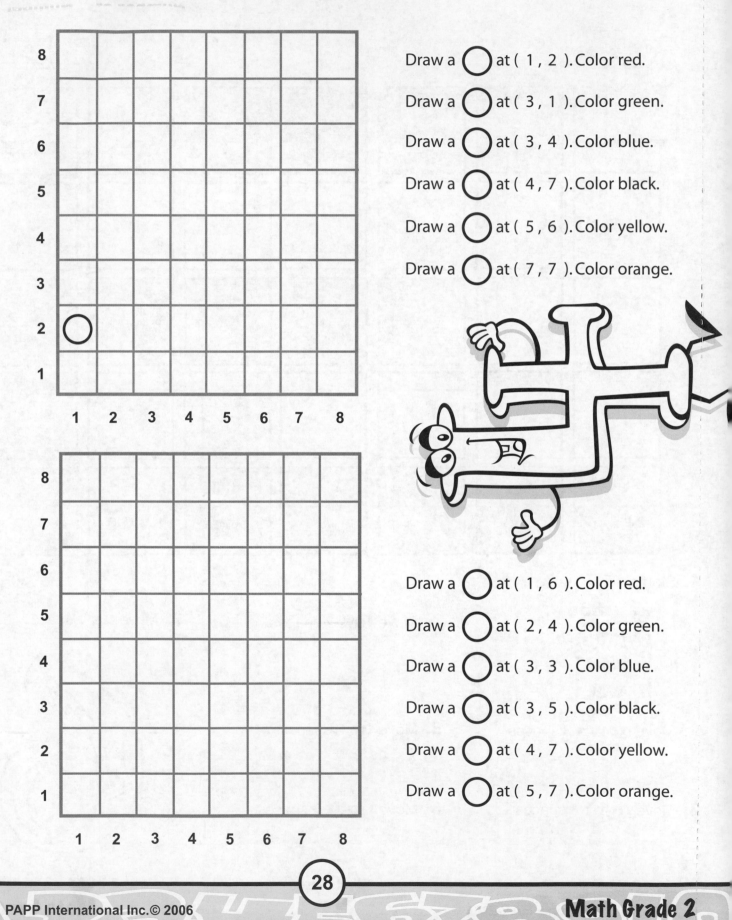

Draw a ◯ at (1 , 2). Color red.

Draw a ◯ at (3 , 1). Color green.

Draw a ◯ at (3 , 4). Color blue.

Draw a ◯ at (4 , 7). Color black.

Draw a ◯ at (5 , 6). Color yellow.

Draw a ◯ at (7 , 7). Color orange.

Draw a ◯ at (1 , 6). Color red.

Draw a ◯ at (2 , 4). Color green.

Draw a ◯ at (3 , 3). Color blue.

Draw a ◯ at (3 , 5). Color black.

Draw a ◯ at (4 , 7). Color yellow.

Draw a ◯ at (5 , 7). Color orange.

Math Grade 2

Exploring Shapes

a. How many sides and angles does each shape have?

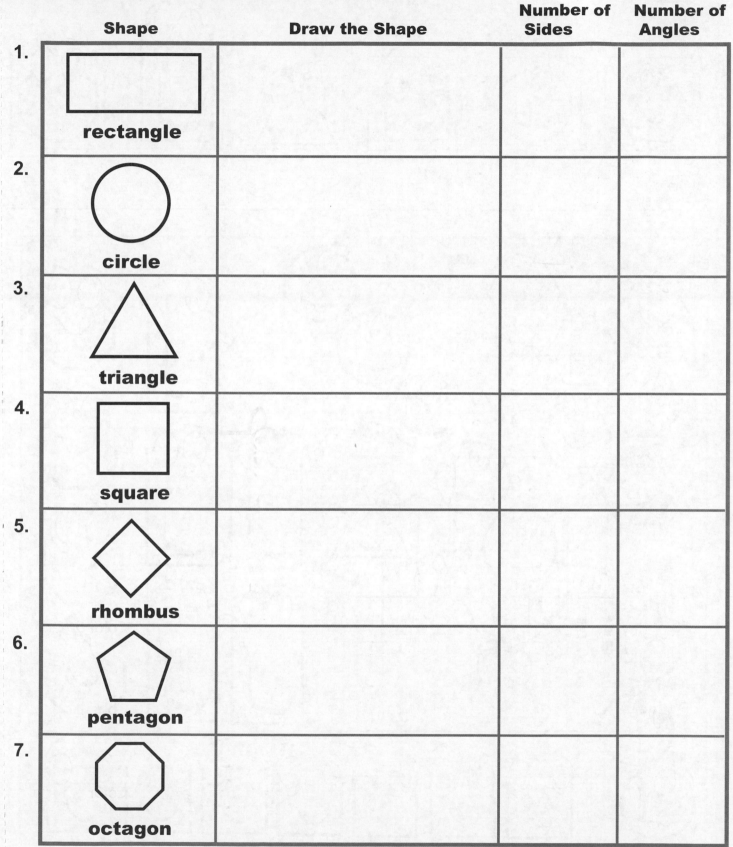

Shape	Draw the Shape	Number of Sides	Number of Angles
1. rectangle			
2. circle			
3. triangle			
4. square			
5. rhombus			
6. pentagon			
7. octagon			

Math Grade 2

a. Look at the picture. How many of each shape do you see?

_____ _____ _____ _____ _____ _____

- -

_____ _____ _____ _____ _____ _____

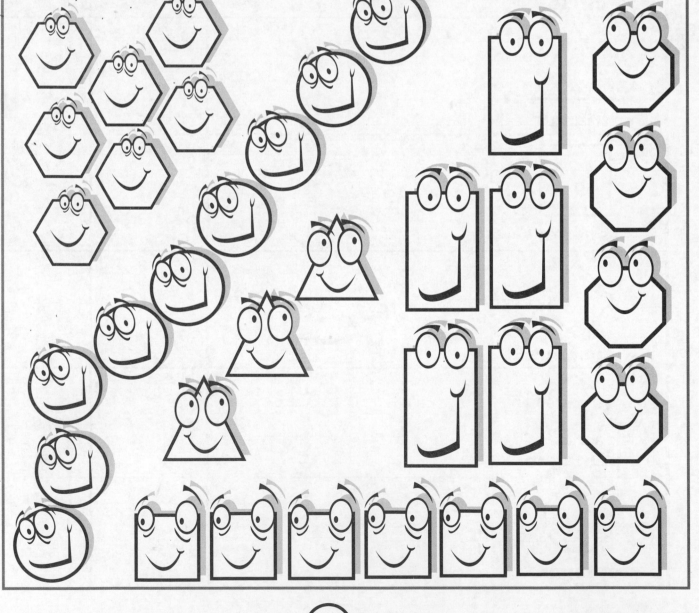

PAPP International Inc.© 2006

Math Grade 2

a. Draw the other half of the picture.

Math Grade 2

a. How long is each object?

1.

2.

3.

Math Grade 2

Exploring Perimeter

a. Find the perimeters.

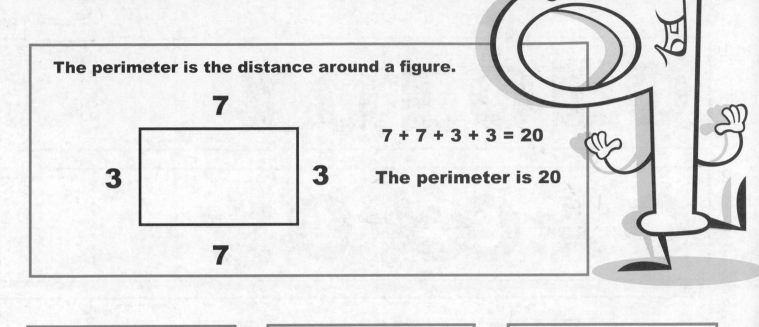

The perimeter is the distance around a figure.

7

3   3

7

7 + 7 + 3 + 3 = 20

The perimeter is 20

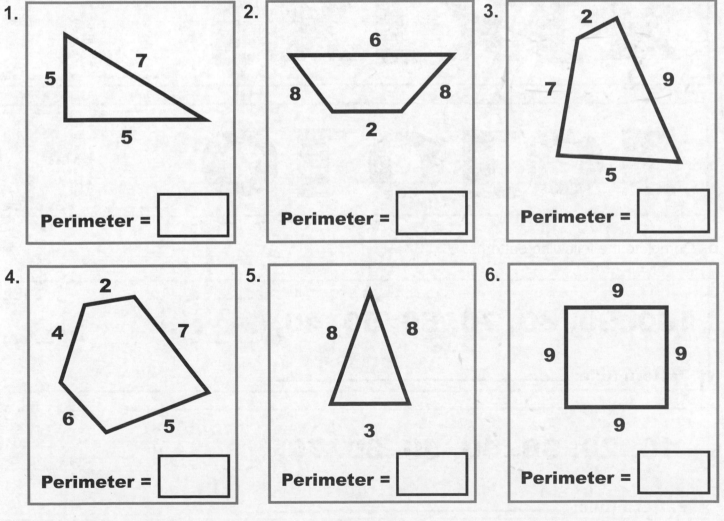

1.

5   7

5

Perimeter = ☐

2.

6

8   8

2

Perimeter = ☐

3.

2

7   9

5

Perimeter = ☐

4.

2

4   7

6   5

Perimeter = ☐

5.

8   8

3

Perimeter = ☐

6.

9

9   9

9

Perimeter = ☐

PAPP International Inc.© 2006

Math Grade 2

Extend the Pattern

a. Finish each pattern.

1. O] O] O] O [ ] [ ]

2. O ✳ O ✳ O ✳ [ ] [ ]

3. X] X] X] X [ ] [ ]

4.] O] O] O] O [ ] [ ]

b. Complete the following patterns:

1. 100, 90, 80, 70, 60, 50, 40, [30], [20], [10]

Pattern Rule: _____

2. 10, 20, 30, 40, 50, 60, 70, [ ], [ ], [ ]

Pattern Rule: _____

PAPP International Inc.© 2006

Math Grade 2

a. Finish each pattern.

1.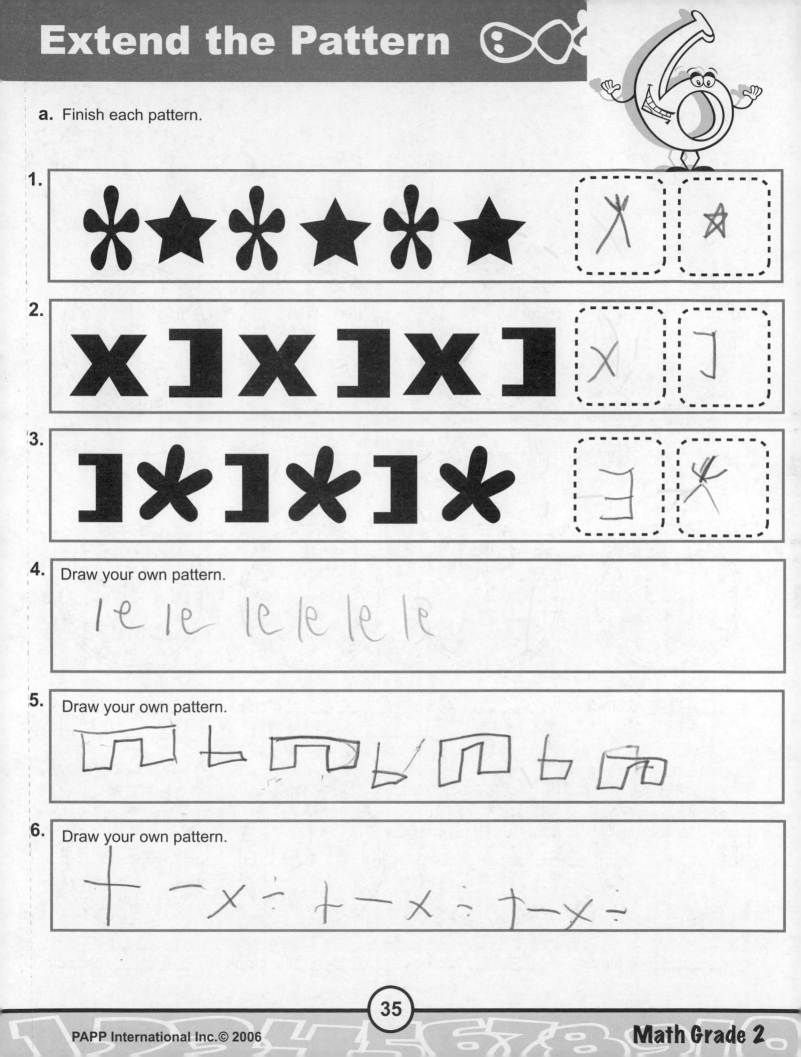

2.

3.

4. Draw your own pattern.

5. Draw your own pattern.

6. Draw your own pattern.

Math Grade 2

Telling Time to the Hour

a. Write the time.

1.

_____ o'clock

2.

_____ o'clock

3.

_____ o'clock

4.

_____ o'clock

5.

_____ o'clock

6.

_____ o'clock

7.

_____ o'clock

8.

_____ o'clock

9.

_____ o'clock

10.

_____ o'clock

11.

_____ o'clock

12.

_____ o'clock

Math Grade 2

a. Write the time.

1. half past _____

2. half past _____

3. half past _____

4. half past _____

5. half past _____

6. half past _____

7. half past _____

8. half past _____

9. half past _____

10. half past _____

11. half past _____

12. half past _____

Math Grade 2

a. Write the time.

1. quarter to __9:30__

2. quarter to __7:45__

3. quarter to __9:45__

4. quarter to __9:20__

5. quarter to __12:45__

6. quarter to __1:45__

7. quarter to __2:45__

8. quarter to __6:45__

9. quarter to __10:9__

10. quarter to __9:49__

11. quarter to __11:95__

12. quarter to __3:45__

Math Grade 2

Month of the Year Word Search

a. Complete the word search.

x	s	e	p	t	e	m	b	e	r	x	d
q	k	q	t	v	v	p	n	m	k	h	a
d	d	n	o	v	e	m	b	e	r	q	p
e	o	k	f	e	b	r	u	a	r	y	r
c	m	o	x	x	t	t	x	m	v	n	i
e	j	d	j	k	m	a	y	x	j	q	l
m	u	v	u	p	v	o	m	h	a	s	o
b	l	n	n	p	m	x	a	h	n	v	v
e	y	k	e	p	v	n	r	k	u	n	k
r	h	h	m	s	u	x	c	x	a	v	x
b	a	u	g	u	s	t	h	x	r	k	p
b	o	c	t	o	b	e	r	x	y	h	d

January   February   March   April

May   June   July   August   September

October   November   December

39

PAPP International Inc.© 2006

Math Grade 2

Answer Page

Answer Key to some of the pages:

Page **2**   Ordering Numbers

(1) 25, 27 (2) 70, 72 (3) 52 (4) 26 (5) 15 (6) 26 (7) 35 (8) 6 (9) 17 (10) 79, 81 (11) 46 (12) 49
(13) 46 (14) 80, 82 (15) 10 (16) 64

Page **3**   Skip Counting

(1) 57, 58, 59 (2) 60, 62, 64 (3) 85, 90, 95 (4) 21, 24, 27 (5) 38, 40, 42 (6) 75, 80, 85 (7) 22, 26, 30
(8) 42, 45, 48

Page **4**   Counting

(1) 16, 15, 14, 13, 12, 11 (2) 9, 10, 11, 12, 13, 14 (3) 22, 21, 20, 19, 18, 17 (4) 12, 13, 14, 15, 16, 17
(5) 11, 12, 13, 14, 15, 16 (6) 19, 18, 17, 16 15, 14 (7) 17, 16, 15 14, 13, 12 (8) 20, 19, 18, 17, 16, 15
(9) 12, 11, 10, 9, 8 , 7

Page **7**   Tens and Ones

a. (1) 1 tens, 3 ones = 13 (2) 2 tens, 9 ones = 29 (3) 4 tens, 4 ones = 44 (4) 8 tens, 0 ones = 80
(5) 7 tens, 3 ones = 73 (6) 5 tens, 7 ones = 57

b. (1) 7 tens, 0 ones = 70 (2) 0 tens, 7 ones = 7 (3) 1 tens, 9 ones = 19 (4) 1 tens, 8 ones = 18

Page **8**   Regrouping Ones and Tens

(1) 4 tens, 12 ones   regroup 5 tens, 2 ones (2) 1 tens, 21 ones   regroup 3 tens, 1 ones
(3) 5 tens, 13 ones   regroup 6 tens, 3 ones (4) 3 tens, 18 ones   regroup 4 tens, 8 ones

Page **9**   Hundreds, Tens and Ones

(1) 1 hundred, 2 tens, 2 ones = 122   (2) 7 hundreds, 7 tens, 4 ones = 774   (3) 6 hundreds, 5 tens, 1 ones = 651
(4) 3 hundreds, 6 tens, 5 ones = 365

Page **10**   Addition Fun

(1) 11 (2) 6 (3) 12 (4) 8 (5) 18 (6) 14 (7) 11 (8) 12 (9) 17 (10) 12 (11) 16 (12) 13
(13) 10 (14) 2 (15) 20 (16) 13 (17) 15 (18) 10 (19) 3 (20) 14

Page **11**   Addition Fun

(1) 5 (2) 2 (3) 2 (4) 5 (5) 9 (6) 8 (7) 2 (8) 6 (9) 7 (10) 5 (11) 9 (12) 0
(13) 2 (14) 4 (15) 3 (16) 7 (17) 1 (18) 3

PAPP International Inc.© 2006

Math Grade 2

Answer Page

Answer Key to some of the pages:

Page **12**   Subtraction Fun

(1) 4 (2) 7 (3) 9 (4) 6 (5) 8 (6) 5 (7) 7 (8) 4 (9) 8 (10) 5 (11) 9 (12) 7
(13) 9 (14) 1 (15) 4 (16) 7 (17) 8 (18) 1

Page **13**   Subtraction Fun

(1) 10 (2) 9 (3) 6 (4) 5 (5) 9 (6) 3 (7) 11 (8) 7 (9) 4 (10) 12 (11) 7 (12) 9
(13) 7 (14) 4 (15) 8 (16) 16 (17) 11 (18) 15

Page **14**   More Addition and Subtraction

(1) 6 (2) 15 (3) 5 (4) 13 (5) 9 (6) 4 (7) 5 (8) 6 (9) 6 (10) 14 (11)10 (12) 3
(13) 10 (14) 1 (15) 12 (16) 17 (17) 5 (18) 5 (19) 8 (20) 7 (21) 12 (22) 8 (23) 14 (24) 9 (25) 15 (26) 6 (27) 7

Page **15**   What's the Sign?

(1) + (2) + (3) - (4) - (5) + (6) - (7) + (8) - (9) + (10) + (11) + (12) - (13) - (14) - (15) - (16) +

Page **16**   Two Digit Addition

(1) 48 (2) 55 (3) 99 (4) 77 (5) 52 (6) 67 (7) 39 (8) 95 (9) 89 (10) 84 (11) 88 (12) 98
(13) 91 (14) 55 (15) 56 (16) 44 (17) 48 (18) 59 (19) 95 (20) 99

Page **17**   Two Digit Addition with Regrouping

(1) 63 (2) 82 (3) 65 (4) 90 (5) 83 (6) 90 (7) 90 (8) 101 (9) 82 (10) 80 (11) 94 (12) 65
(13) 81 (14) 92 (15) 83

Page **18**   Two Digit Subtraction without Borrowing

(1) 12 (2) 22 (3) 11 (4) 31 (5) 33 (6) 41 (7) 82 (8) 41 (9) 10 (10) 71 (11) 12 (12) 25
(13) 41 (14) 15 (15) 50 (16) 35 (17) 71 (18) 11 (19) 10 (20) 25

Page **19**   Subtraction with Borrowing

(1) 25 (2) 15 (3) 55 (4) 56 (5) 28 (6) 28 (7) 37 (8) 37 (9) 29 (10) 9 (11) 16 (12) 9
(13) 29 (14) 46 (15) 31

PAPP International Inc.© 2006   **Math Grade 2**

Answer Page

Answer Key to some of the pages:

Page **20**   Addition and Multiplication

(1) 6, 6 (2) 15, 15 (3) 12, 12 (4) 16, 16 (5) 14, 14 (6) 12, 12

Page **21**   Introducing Division

(1) 3 (2) 6 (3) 4 (4) 2 (5) 3 (6) 2

Page **22**   Fractions

(1) $\frac{1}{2}$ (2) $\frac{1}{4}$ (3) $\frac{1}{3}$ (4) $\frac{1}{3}$ (5) $\frac{1}{2}$ (6) $\frac{1}{4}$ (7) $\frac{1}{2}$ (8) $\frac{1}{4}$ (9) $\frac{1}{3}$ (10) $\frac{1}{3}$ (11) $\frac{1}{3}$ (12) $\frac{1}{4}$

Page **23**   Show the Fractions

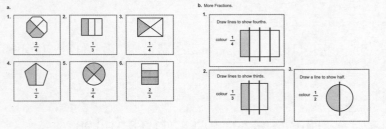

Page **24**   Graph 1

(1) 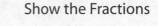 (2)   (3) 13 people (4) 5 people (5) triangle, circle, hexagon, square

Page **25**   Graph 2

(1)   (2)   (3) 15 people (4) 3 people (5) 2, 3, 1, 1

Page **26**   Graph 3

(1)   (2)   (3) 14 people (4) 3 people (5) 4, 1, 3, 2

Page **27**   Read and Follow the Directions

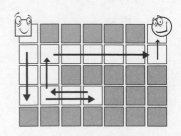

PAPP International Inc.© 2006   **Math Grade 2**

Answer Page

Answer Key to some of the pages:

Page **28**   Exploring Grids

Page **29**   Exploring Shapes

(1) Rectangle   Number of Sides 4   Number of Angles 4
(2) Circle   Number of Sides 0   Number of Angles 0
(3) Triangle   Number of Sides 3   Number of Angles 3
(4) Square   Number of Sides 4   Number of Angles 4
(5) Rhombus   Number of Sides 4   Number of Angles 4
(6) Pentagon   Number of Sides 5   Number of Angles 5
(7) Octagon   Number of Sides 8   Number of Angles 8

Page **30**   Shape Count

(1) 7, 9, 7, 3, 5, 4

Page **32**   Non Standard Measuring

(1) about 3 (2) about 7 (3) about 5

Page **33**   Exploring Perimeter

(1) 17 (2) 24 (3) 23 (4) 24 (5) 19 (6) 36

Page **34**   Extend Patterns

a.

b.
1. Pattern rule -10
   30, 20 , 10

2. Pattern rule +10
   80, 90 , 100

Page **35**   Extend Patterns

Page **36**   Telling Time to the Hour

(1) 12 (2) 7 (3) 1 (4) 3 (5) 6 (6) 11 (7) 5 (8) 2 (9) 10 (10) 8 (11) 4 (12) 9

Page **37**   Telling Time to the Half Hour

(1) 11 (2) 3 (3) 7 (4) 12 (5) 4 (6) 9: (7) 10 (8) 5 (9) 8 (10) 1 (11) 6 (12) 2

Page **38**   Telling Time to the Quarter Hour

(1) 7 (2) 8 (3) 10 (4) 5 (5) 1 (6) 2
(7) 3 (8) 6 (9) 11 (10) 10 (11) 12 (12) 4

Page **39**   Month of the Year Word Search

PAPP International Inc.© 2006

Math Grade 2

Congratulations on completing **Math Grade** 2

GREAT WORK!

Name:

44